© Alexandra Goreing
sagoreingverde@email.wm.edu
ISBN: 9781709495632
1st edition, December 2019
Graphic Design: Yolanda Carlessi
Translation: Alexandra Goreing
Illustrated by Guillermo Izaguirre

A Story for Children
Written by a Young Girl

The Author

Alex is an 8-year-old girl who traveled extensively with her parents at a young age. She loves reading and is always carrying a book under her arm. She also loves music, nature and animals. She is eager to discover the world and always ready for the next adventure!

Life as an Ashaninka, what an adventure!

Alexandra Goreing

Illustrated by Guillermo Izaguirre

One beautiful, sunny day I logged into my computer to see if I had any e-mails from my pen pals. Amongst all the e-mails I received, I found one from my Japanese friend Susu, in which she wrote: "Alexandra, my teacher gave me a homework assignment to study the Amazon rainforest; I need to know how a native Ashaninka family lives there. Can you send me information please?"

I answered her immediately, saying: "It must be difficult in Japan to find information about the Amazon, so I will do some research on the flora and fauna of the Peruvian rainforest to help you."

When Susu read my e-mail, she replied: "Thanks for your help! Send me all the information as soon as you have it please. Bye-bye!"

After I finished reading my e-mails, I started reading my parents' books about the many places to visit in the Peruvian Amazon. Then, I had an idea! I decided to ask my mother if I could take a trip to the rainforest to learn more about it in person. Mother told me that she would have to think about it the rest of the afternoon and that she would give me an answer before bedtime.

I was in my room later that night when suddenly: "knock-knock!" Mother was at the door; she had come to give me an answer. "I have made a decision," she said, "Susu has helped you many times with things that you needed, and that is why I have decided to let you go to the rainforest for a couple of days. I have made the arrangements. Tomorrow, a tour guide will pick you up to go to the airport. Then, he will take you to the house of a very well-known Ashaninka family name Shapiama. You will stay with them for two days. Pack your things because you are leaving early tomorrow morning!"

I started packing my backpack, thinking about the jungle: What would it be like? How would I feel when I am there? That night, I dreamt of myself floating in a canoe down the long Amazon River with rainforest animals and giant trees all around me. Everything was so exciting!

I woke up the next day ready for my adventure! Mr. Benito, the tour guide, arrived at the house to pick me up. I said goodbye to mother and father, grabbed my backpack and hopped into the car. Halfway

to the airport, I started wondering what the homes of the Ashaninkas would look like.

At the airport, I passed security and sat in the waiting room. I bought some sweets, and when it was the time to board the plane, I picked up my backpack and stood first in line! The flight attendant asked me "Where are you going?" I said: "I'm going to Loreto! That is where the Ashaninka Tribe lives."

On the plane, I found my seat and started writing in my notebook all my ideas about what the rain forest looked like, because I had never been there before. After a three-hour flight, we arrived at the Iquitos airport in Loreto, where I showed my passport once again. When I finally went outside, the weather was very hot! I thought I was going to melt!

I hopped into the waiting car and we drove until we reached the end of the dirt road. The rest of the path was accessible only by foot. It was a long walk to the house of the Shapiama family, we crossed bridges and rivers and were caught in a heavy rain shower that soaked us all from head to toe. We finally arrived around 5:00 p.m., very tired from the journey. The rain forest looked a lot like what I had imagined and written about in my notebook.

Once I arrived, I met the Shapiama family. The mother's name was Wasai and her daughter was Japipi. Japipi was my age; she had a monkey, Maui, who was very playful and funny. Japipi liked to make clay vases with her hands and ride in the canoe. She loved animals and took the responsibility of feeding them. When she finished telling me about her hobbies, her father, Mr. Shaijame, arrived with a fresh fish for dinner. While eating, they fed fruits to Maui. The food was fresh and I enjoyed it very much. Soon, it was time for bed. I changed into my pajamas and climbed into my hammock to sleep.

The next day, I woke up at 5:00 a.m. Japipi and I went with Maui to pick a variety of exotic and delicious fruit that I had never tried before. We ate them for breakfast and drank a delicious aguaje juice. We gave Maui a banana, he likes them very much. After breakfast, Japipi showed me how to make clay pots before we went to feed the other animals.

Japipi and her mother taught me how to make clothes with painted designs similar to the ones they were wearing. While we waited for our painted clothes to dry, we went to plant vegetables. Mr. Shaijame went again in his canoe to fish; when he returned, it was time for lunch. We went to the river to wash our hands before lunch. We drank fresh orange juice and ate a delicious salad made with chonta

12

(which is the heart of the palm tree) accompanied by Paiche (a large river fish). After lunch, Japipi and I went back to explore the river in her canoe. We saw many exotic animals that I had only seen in photos before – toucans, frogs, pink dolphins and a yellow jaguar. Japipi was paddling and telling me about how her family lives in harmony with the animals. We went near the banks to rest for a while when suddenly I saw a creature that I had never seen before, it looked like a humongous guinea pig! I didn't know what it was, so I asked Japipi "What's that?" She replied, "That animal is a Capybara." "Why does it look like a guinea pig?" "Well," she explained, "the Capybara is a family member of the guinea pig, and it is the largest rodent in the world! They love to swim and live near the water, that's why we are seeing it, they are very social animals."

When we finished our trip, we returned to the house. Mr. Shaijame went out again to fish, this time he caught a Dorado fish. We ate the fish with fried cassava for dinner, and drank a traditional drink made from peanuts. While we ate, they told me very interesting stories about their lifestyle. After dinner, the Tribe played some music as we danced around the fire.

The next day, I woke up really early again and we repeated yesterday's routine. When we finished our chores, we started making pots out of

clay. Time passed quickly, I didn't realize it was
already time to leave.

Mr. Benito arrived on time to pick me up,
I said goodbye to the Shapiama family,
thanking them for all their kind attention
during my stay. They had a surprise for me
to take home: a baby capybara!
I named him Shaimau, I carried him in my arms and
went to the car, I told them that I would come back very soon.
I was ready to go home. I realized that it is very tiring to live like an
Ashaninka.

We arrived at the airport and took the plane to return to Lima. Once in
Lima, I rode in the car with my baby capybara in my arms the entire way
until I arrived home. I knocked on the door and shouted "Surprise!" My
parents looked from the window and came quickly when they saw the
baby capybara, they were very anxious to hear about my adventure.

But I was forgetting something! I had to send all the information
about the Ashaninkas to my friend Susu. I left Shaimau with my mom
to write to Susu when suddenly, I heard my mom exclaim: "To have
a capybara in the house, what a hassle!"

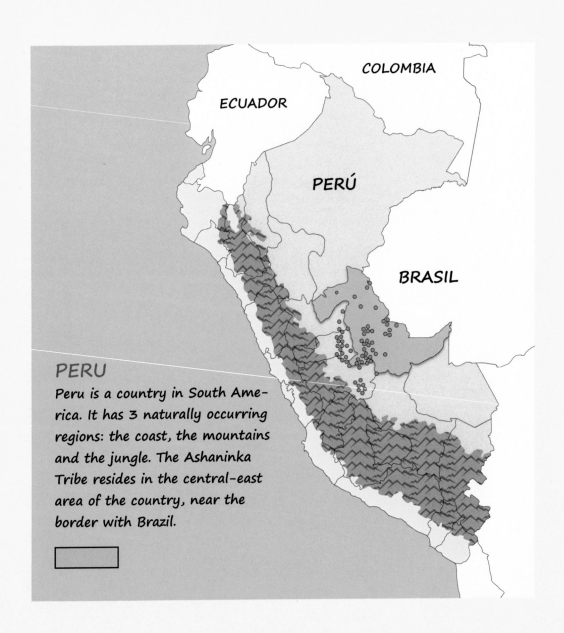

COLOMBIA

ECUADOR

PERÚ

BRASIL

PERU

Peru is a country in South America. It has 3 naturally occurring regions: the coast, the mountains and the jungle. The Ashaninka Tribe resides in the central-east area of the country, near the border with Brazil.

VOCABULARY

ASHANINKA.- Indigenous people who live in the rainforest of Peru.

AGUAJE.- Reddish brown fruit with a scaly covering and a deep yellow pulp inside.

CHICHA.- Beverage usually derived from grain, maize or fruit.

CHONTA.- Palm shoots.

CUY.- Latin America guinea pig.

OTORONGO- Jaguar from the Andes.

PAICHE- Found in the Amazon River, the Paiche is the largest freshwater fish in the world.

RONSOCO- South American Capybara, the largest living rodent.

YUCA- Root of the Cassava plant.